Happy Birthday Syd, Alistair 2016

MANGA SHAKESPEARE®

MACBETH

D0333972

ADAPTED BY
RICHARD APPIGNANESI

ILLUSTRATED BY
ROBERT DEAS

**SELF
MADE
HERO**

Published by
SelfMadeHero
A division of Metro Media Ltd
139–141 Pancras Raod
London NW1 1UN
www.selfmadehero.com

This edition published 2015

Illustrator: Robert Deas
Text Adaptor: Richard Appignanesi
Designer: Andy Huckle
Textual Consultant: Nick de Somogyi
Publisher: Emma Hayley

ISBN: 978-0-9552856-6-0

10 9 8 7 6
Printed and bound in Slovenia

Macbeth and Lady Macbeth

"But screw your courage to the sticking-place and we'll not fail!"

"I dare do all that may become a man."

Macduff, another warlord loyal to King Duncan

"Bring this fiend within my sword's length!"

WHEN SHALL WE THREE MEET AGAIN? IN THUNDER, LIGHTNING OR IN RAIN?

WHEN THE HURLYBURLY'S DONE, WHEN THE BATTLE'S LOST AND WON.

BUT ALL'S TOO WEAK, FOR BRAVE MACBETH WITH BRANDISHED STEEL CARVED OUT HIS PASSAGE TILL HE FACED THE SLAVE.

19

29

THE PRINCE OF CUMBERLAND!

THAT IS A STEP ON WHICH I MUST FALL DOWN, OR ELSE OVERLEAP, FOR IN MY WAY IT LIES.

STARS, HIDE YOUR FIRES! LET NOT LIGHT SEE MY BLACK AND DEEP DESIRES.

LET THAT BE WHICH THE EYE FEARS, WHEN IT IS DONE, TO SEE.

MACBETH SENDS NEWS OF HIS SUCCESS TO HIS WIFE, LADY MACBETH...

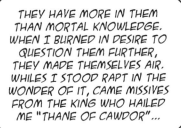

THEY HAVE MORE IN THEM THAN MORTAL KNOWLEDGE. WHEN I BURNED IN DESIRE TO QUESTION THEM FURTHER, THEY MADE THEMSELVES AIR. WHILES I STOOD RAPT IN THE WONDER OF IT, CAME MISSIVES FROM THE KING WHO HAILED ME "THANE OF CAWDOR"...

... BY WHICH TITLE, BEFORE, THESE WEIRD SISTERS SALUTED ME, AND REFERRED ME TO THE COMING ON OF TIME WITH "HAIL, KING THAT SHALT BE!" THIS HAVE I THOUGHT GOOD TO DELIVER THEE, MY DEAREST PARTNER OF GREATNESS.

DUNCAN HATH BEEN SO CLEAR IN HIS GREAT OFFICE THAT HIS VIRTUES WILL PLEAD LIKE ANGELS TRUMPET-TONGUED.

I HAVE GIVEN SUCK AND KNOW HOW TENDER 'TIS TO LOVE THE BABE THAT MILKS ME.

I WOULD, WHILE IT WAS SMILING IN MY FACE, HAVE PLUCKED MY NIPPLE FROM HIS BONELESS GUMS AND DASHED THE BRAINS OUT — HAD I SO SWORN AS YOU HAVE DONE TO THIS.

71

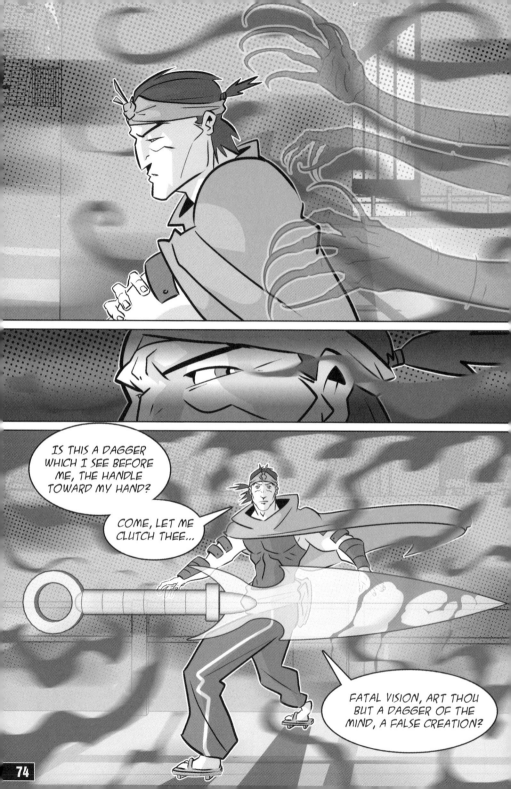

79

85

YOUR ROYAL FATHER'S MURDERED.

O! BY WHOM?

THOSE OF HIS CHAMBER, AS IT SEEMED, HAD DONE IT.

THEIR HANDS AND FACES WERE ALL BADGED WITH BLOOD.

O, I DO REPENT ME OF MY FURY THAT I DID KILL THEM.

WHEREFORE DID YOU SO?

97

119

KRAKA-BOOM

BE BLOODY, BOLD AND RESOLUTE! NONE OF WOMAN BORN SHALL HARM MACBETH.

THEN LIVE, MACDUFF — WHAT NEED I FEAR OF THEE?

BUT YET I'LL MAKE DOUBLE SURE: THOU SHALT NOT LIVE.

137

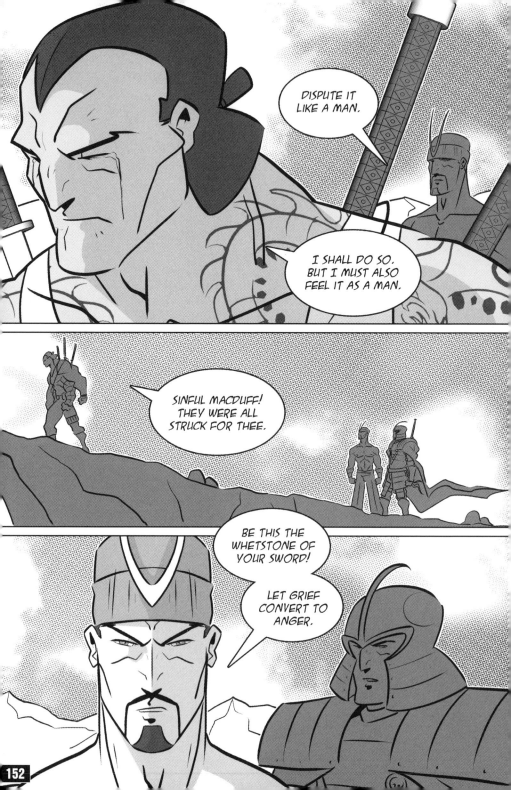

THE SPIRITS THAT KNOW ALL MORTAL CONSEQUENCES HAVE PRONOUNCED ME THUS...

"FEAR NOT, MACBETH!"

"NO MAN THAT'S BORN OF WOMAN SHALL EVER HAVE POWER UPON THEE."

171

175

190

THEN YIELD THEE, COWARD, AND LIVE TO BE THE SHOW AND GAZE OF THE TIME.

WE'LL HAVE THEE, AS OUR RARER MONSTERS ARE, ON A POLE — AND UNDERWRIT, "HERE MAY YOU SEE THE TYRANT."

THOUGH BIRNAM WOOD BE COME TO DUNSINANE, AND THOU BEING OF NO WOMAN BORN, YET I WILL TRY THE LAST.

LAY ON, MACDUFF, AND DAMNED BE HIM THAT FIRST CRIES, "HOLD, ENOUGH!"

WE SHALL NOT SPEND A LARGE EXPENSE OF TIME BEFORE WE MAKE US EVEN WITH YOU.
MY KINSMEN, HENCEFORTH BE EARLS, THE FIRST EVER IN SUCH AN HONOUR NAMED, WHOM WE INVITE TO SEE US CROWNED.
WHAT'S MORE TO DO, AS CALLING HOME OUR EXILED FRIENDS THAT FLED THE SNARES OF THIS DEAD BUTCHER AND HIS FIEND-LIKE QUEEN, WHO BY SELF-VIOLENT HANDS TOOK OFF HER LIFE...

THIS AND WHAT ELSE, BY THE GRACE OF GRACE,

WE WILL PERFORM IN MEASURE, TIME, AND PLACE.

205

PLOT SUMMARY OF MACBETH

The rule of good King Duncan has been saved from rebel forces: his loyal warlords, Macbeth and Banquo, have triumphed in battle over an invading army, and the traitorous Thane of Cawdor is among the prisoners. Returning home, Macbeth and Banquo encounter three witches, who deliver a series of prophecies: Macbeth will inherit the Thane of Cawdor's title and will become king; Banquo will father a dynasty of kings, though will never himself be king.

Duncan orders the execution of the captured Thane of Cawdor, bestowing that title on Macbeth – and this fulfilment of the first of the witches' prophecies stirs Macbeth's ambition. He confides in his wife, Lady Macbeth, who persuades him to murder Duncan as he sleeps.

When Duncan's body is discovered, Macbeth kills the dead king's bodyguards, and Duncan's sons, Malcolm and Donalbain, flee in fear of their lives. Now crowned king, Macbeth acts to prevent Banquo's descendants becoming kings. Banquo is brutally killed in an ambush – but his son, Fleance, escapes.

Tormented by a vision of Banquo's bloody ghost, Macbeth seeks out the three witches, who seem to offer reassurance: Macbeth, they say, cannot be harmed by anyone "of woman born", and can rest secure until the great forest of Birnam Wood "come to Dunsinane". Feeling himself immune, Macbeth dispatches assassins to murder the family of Macduff (one of Duncan's warlords), who has fled to join forces with Malcolm.

News of his family's slaughter is brought to Macduff during an interview with Malcolm. United in their grief, they march with their armies to overthrow Macbeth. Meanwhile, Lady Macbeth's guilt has driven her to insanity and suicide. Macbeth staves off despair by remembering the witches' prophecy... until the impossible news arrives that Birnam Wood is approaching Dunsinane: Malcolm's armies have camouflaged themselves with its branches.

In the ensuing battle, Macbeth fights valiantly – until he encounters Macduff, who declares that he is not "of woman born": his birth was by Caesarean section.

Macbeth has been misled by the witches. He is slain and beheaded by Macduff. Malcolm is proclaimed king. And, as Shakespeare's first audiences would have known, Fleance's descendants included their own royal family. And our own.

A BRIEF LIFE OF WILLIAM SHAKESPEARE

Shakespeare's birthday is traditionally said to be the 23rd of April – St George's Day, patron saint of England. A good start for England's greatest writer. But that date and even his name are uncertain. He signed his own name in different ways. "Shakespeare" is now the accepted one out of dozens of different versions.

He was born at Stratford-upon-Avon in 1564, and baptized on 26th April. His mother, Mary Arden, was the daughter of a prosperous farmer. His father, John Shakespeare, a glove-maker, was a respected civic figure – and probably also a Catholic. In 1570, just as Will began school, his father was accused of illegal dealings. The family fell into debt and disrepute.

Will attended a local school for eight years. He did not go to university. The next ten years are a blank filled by suppositions. Was he briefly a Latin teacher, a soldier, a sea-faring explorer? Was he prosecuted and whipped for poaching deer?

We do know that in 1582 he married Anne Hathaway, eight years his senior, and three months pregnant. Two more children – twins – were born three years later but, by around 1590, Will had left Stratford to pursue a theatre career in London. Shakespeare's apprenticeship began as an actor and "pen for hire".

He learned his craft the hard way. He soon won fame as a playwright with often-staged popular hits.

He and his colleagues formed a stage company, the Lord Chamberlain's Men, which built the famous Globe Theatre. It opened in 1599 but was destroyed by fire in 1613 during a performance of *Henry VIII* which used gunpowder special effects. It was rebuilt in brick the following year.

Shakespeare was a financially successful writer who invested his money wisely in property. In 1597, he bought an enormous house in Stratford, and in 1608 became a shareholder in London's Blackfriars Theatre. He also redeemed the family's honour by acquiring a personal coat of arms.

Shakespeare wrote over 40 works, including poems, "lost" plays and collaborations, in a career spanning nearly 25 years. He retired to Stratford in 1613, where he died on 23rd April 1616, aged 52, apparently of a fever after a "merry meeting" of drinks with friends. Shakespeare did in fact die on St George's Day! He was buried "full 17 foot deep" in Holy Trinity Church, Stratford, and left an epitaph cursing anyone who dared disturb his bones.

There have been preposterous theories disputing Shakespeare's authorship. Some claim that Sir Francis Bacon (1561–1626), philosopher and Lord Chancellor, was the real author of Shakespeare's plays. Others propose Edward de Vere, Earl of Oxford (1550–1604), or, even more weirdly, Queen Elizabeth I. The implication is that the "real" Shakespeare had to be a university graduate or an aristocrat. Nothing less would do for the world's greatest writer.

Shakespeare is mysteriously hidden behind his work. His life will not tell us what inspired his genius.

MANGA SHAKESPEARE ®

EDITORIAL

Richard Appignanesi: Text Adaptor

Richard Appignanesi was a founder and co-director of the Writers & Readers Publishing Cooperative and Icon Books where he originated the internationally acclaimed *Introducing* series. His own best-selling titles in the series include *Freud*, *Postmodernism* and *Existentialism*. He is also the author of the fiction trilogy *Italia Perversa* and the novel *Yukio Mishima's Report to the Emperor*. Currently associate editor of the journal *Third Text* and reviews editor of the journal *Futures*, his latest book *What do Existentialists Believe?* was released in 2006.

Nick de Somogyi: Textual Consultant

Nick de Somogyi works as a freelance writer and researcher, as a genealogist at the College of Arms, and as a contributing editor to *New Theatre Quarterly*. He is the founding editor of the *Globe Quartos* series, and was the visiting curator at Shakespeare's Globe, 2003–6. His publications include *Shakespeare's Theatre of War* (1998), *Jokermen and Thieves: Bob Dylan and the Ballad Tradition* (1986), and (from 2001) the *Shakespeare Folios* series for Nick Hern Books. He has also contributed to the Open University (1995), Carlton Television (2000), and BBC Radio 3 and Radio 4.

ARTIST

Robert Deas

Robert Deas is a new face of the emerging UK manga scene. He started his career drawing webcomics including the sci-fi epic, *Instrument of War*, currently a 148-page webcomic. A spin off, *Unity Rising*, came second in the print comic category at last year's prestigious IMAF competition and is set to appear in *The Mammoth Book of Best New Manga 3*. His sci-fi espionage story, *November*, was featured in *The Mammoth Book of Best New Manga 2*. Robert has also had his work exhibited in the Japanese Embassy as part of the Manga Jiman exhibition.

PUBLISHER

SelfMadeHero is a UK-based manga and graphic novel imprint, reinventing some of the most important works of European and world literature.

MANGA SHAKESPEARE TITLES

Romeo and Juliet, Hamlet, The Tempest, A Midsummer Night's Dream, Richard III, Julius Caesar, Othello, Twelfth Night, The Merchant of Venice, Henry VIII, King Lear, As You Like It, Macbeth, Much Ado About Nothing.

SELF MADE HERO

www.selfmadehero.com